your time to SHINE

Brilliant steps

Before you start, gather together pencils and pens. Find a quiet place to sit together – preferably at a table, to teach your child the correct posture for working throughout his or her school years.

Start at the beginning of the book and work through it in page order. *Time to Shine* has been written so that it introduces your child to concepts in careful progression. If he or she wants to stop after the first activity, do so, and then reintroduce the book another day. Don't spend too long on one type of activity; try to vary the things you do together as this will show your child that games and playing together can be a learning experience as well.

Most of all, emphasise the fun element of what you are doing. Praise his or her attempts, use the motivational reward chart at the back of this book to help encourage effort, and enjoy this special and exciting time!

Encourage your child to hold the pencil correctly whenever he or she is drawing or writing.

5 alive

Here are the numbers 1 to 10.
Can you count from one to ten?

1 2 3 4 5
6 7 8 9 10

Point to each number and read it out loud to help with number recognition.

Can you count the animals in the pet shop?

Help your child count by pointing to each animal in turn.

What is missing? Can you draw and colour the correct number of blocks in the space?

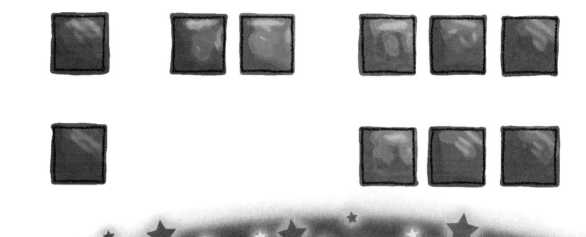

The juggler has got the numbers in the wrong order! Write the numbers in the correct order at the bottom of the page.

Count with your child and work out the pattern before he or she starts to draw.

Point out the numbers at the top of the opposite page for your child to copy.

Give lots of praise and stick the first reward sticker in the chart.

Rhyme time

Look at these pictures. Can you tell what rhyme the pictures show?

1, 2, 3, 4, 5,
Once I caught a fish alive.

6, 7, 8, 9, 10,
Then I let it go again.

Why did you let it go? Because it bit my finger so. Which finger did it bite? This little finger on my right.

Point to the numbers as you say the rhyme.

Count the numbers out loud.

Read the whole rhyme, encouraging your child to say it aloud with you.

Count these things. Draw a line to connect each picture to its number.

4   **ducklings**

1   **bubbles**

waterlily   2   **bulrushes**   3

your time to SHINE

Count the balls and write the number in the box?

More, more, more

Count the things on each plate and trace the correct number each time.

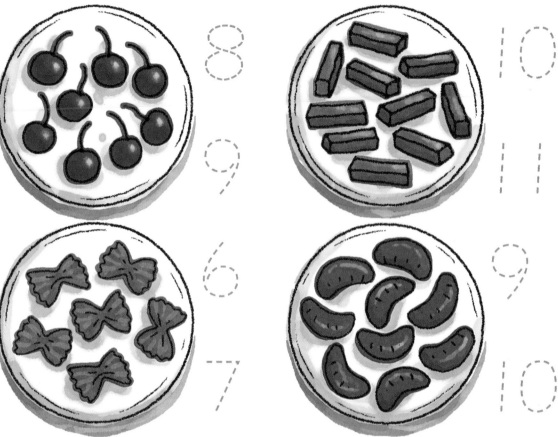

Count the sandwiches in each lunchbox. Then, continue by counting the sandwiches outside each lunchbox. Write the total numbers on the lids.

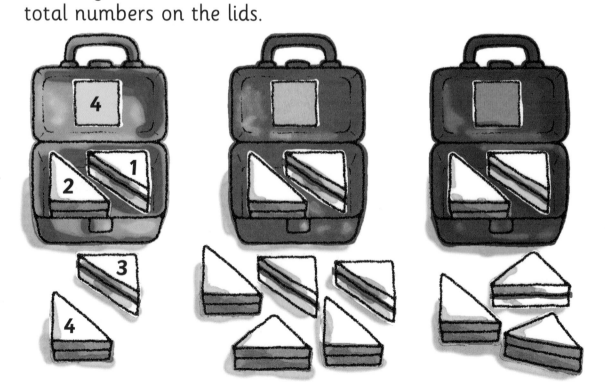

The number on each piggy bank shows you how many coins it contains. Continue counting more coins next to each piggy. Write the totals in each box.

Make sure your child says the first number and continues counting from there.

your time to SHINE

Can you continue counting on these number snakes?

Encourage your child to count out loud.

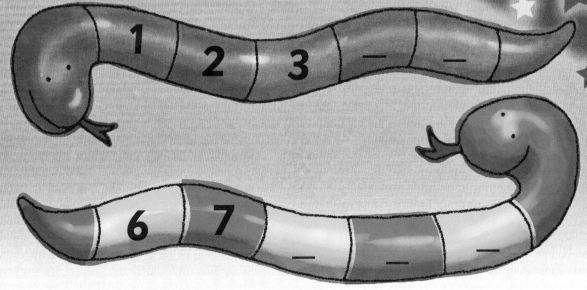

Add a star sticker to the reward chart.

Two by two

Count the number of wheels. Write the numbers in the boxes above the bicycles.

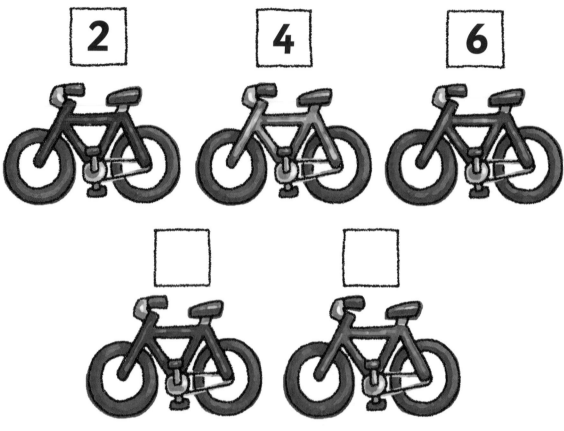

Count the wheels to help add on two each time.

Draw two more circles on each bucket.

Refer your child back to the line of bicycles to help them count up in twos.

Ten fat sausages sizzling in a pan,
One went POP! and another went BANG!

Eight fat sausages sizzling in a pan,
One went POP! and another went BANG!

Your time to SHINE

What number is missing?

6   8   [ ]

12   14   16

Pair them up

Can you draw lines to match the dominoes that are the same?

Draw a circle around each pair of wellies.
Both wellies in a pair have the same number of dots.

This activity is working toward matching pairs by sight, without having to count the dots each time.

If necessary, guide your child by pointing out a boot with a few dots and asking if they can see its partner.

Which are there more of, cups or saucers?

your time to SHINE

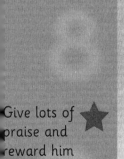

Find two matching groups that make a total of 10.

Zero to hero

There are a couple of zeros missing from this number line. Can you write them in?

Read these numbers out loud. Which one is the highest, or biggest, number? Which is the lowest, or smallest?

Point out that zero is the first number before 1, and that it makes up part of the number 10.

Tell your child that zero is another word for none, or 0.

Let your child attempt to read the numbers first, then read them aloud together

Join the dots to show
the hidden picture.

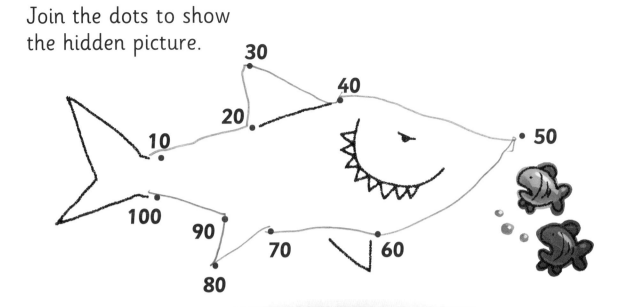

your time to SHINE

These aliens are having a jumping competition!

40
80
10
50
70
100
30
60
90
20

Draw lines to show the correct order they should jump
into the craters. Start at 10 and finish at 100.

More or less?

Which of the animals in each pair has more legs?

Count the legs with your child and then repeat the question: which has more legs?

Draw a circle around each gingerbread person that has more than 3 buttons.

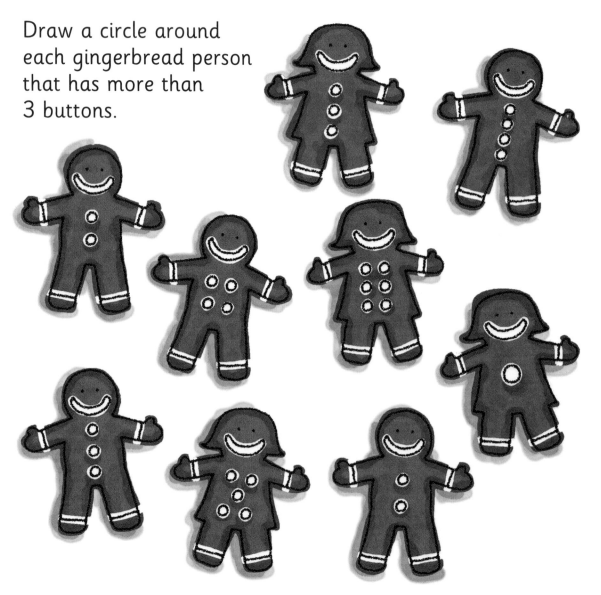

Afterwards, encourage your child to point out those with less than 3 buttons.

Which of the boxes below has **more** eggs in it than the one here. Colour the box blue.

Which of the boxes below has **less** eggs in it? Colour the box yellow.

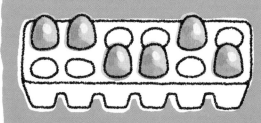

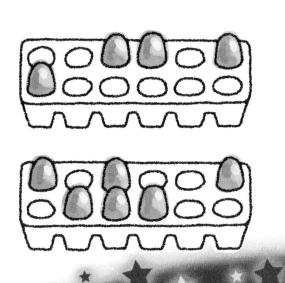

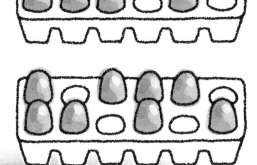

your time to SHINE

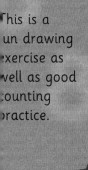

Each snowflake should have 6 points.

Which snowflakes are incomplete? Can you finish them?

Counting backwards

These clowns are learning to count backwards. Can you read their numbers out loud? Where should clown number 6 stand?

Sing the song out loud, and cross out each monkey as he falls off the bed.

Five little monkeys jumping on the bed - one fell off and bumped his head. Mummy called the doctor and the doctor said, "No more monkeys jumping on the bed!"

Counting backwards in general game-playing; 3-2-1-GO! is a great way to reinforce this knowledge.

Repeat the rhyme until there are no monkeys left.

Other counting backwards songs, such as Ten Green Bottles, make learning great fun.

Write the numbers on these medals. Start with the number 10 and work backwards to number 1.

your time to SHINE

Can you complete these number patterns?

8	7	6	5	4	3

14 12 10 8 6 4

60 50 40 30 20

Plus and minus

Draw one more bubble for each fish. Then write how many bubbles there are. Use the number line to help you.

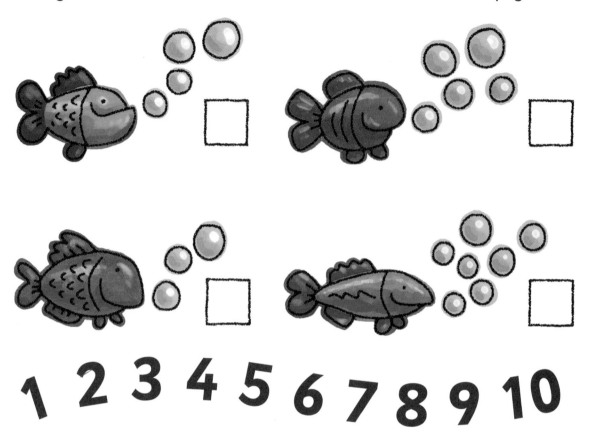

1 2 3 4 5 6 7 8 9 10

Look at the number each monster is holding up. Draw that many more eyes to make each monster look really scary!

Make sure you repeat "Draw one more" each time to reinforce the idea here.

Count on from the original number of eyes as your child draws in the extras.

Cross out a star on each flag to make one less.
How many stars are left on each flag?

5

3

8

4

ach time,
peat the
unting
rase,
X is one
ss than X".
or example:
5 is one less
an 6."

se the
umber line
n the opposite
age to help
ur child.

your time to SHINE

Write what is one more than:

5 6   2 3   7 8   4 5

Write what is one less than:

8 7   3 2   5 4   9 8

Measuring up

Which ruler is longer? Circle it every time.

Compare these things:

Which is the shortest ladder?

Which is the tallest tree?

Which is the longest trumpet?

Which is the smallest mouse?

Draw a circle around the tallest child.

your time to SHINE

How much shorter is the top piece of wood?

How much taller is the first building?

How much longer is the red drumstick?

First prize!

The red frog is first. What colour is the second frog? And the third frog? Carry on until you reach the tenth one.

first   second   third   fourth   fifth

sixth   seventh   eighth   ninth   tenth

This task teaches ordina numbers. Read them out loud with your child Encourage you child to repeat the numbers as he or she names the colours.

Use the instructions to colour in these magic wands.

The **third** wand is **red**.

The **first** wand is **pink**.

The **second** wand is **purple**.

The **fourth** wand is **yellow**.

Read the instructions and let your child decide which is the correct one to colour each time.

Write the order of the racing cars.

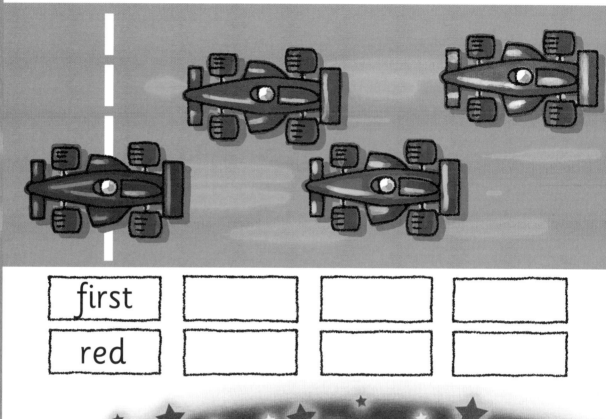

first			
red			

your time to SHINE

Who wins this race?
Use the clues to help you work it out.

The boat in fourth place has a number on it.
The second boat has a star on the back.
The boat that comes third is red at the front.

Colour by numbers

Use the colour key below to colour in this picture.

Can you see what is blasting off?

● = 2, 4, 6, 8   ● = 20, 30, 40, 50

● = 11, 12, 13, 14   ● = 3, 5, 7, 9

WELL DONE! It's your time to shine - you've finished the book.

Congratulate your child on finishing the book.

If the two of you have enjoyed workir together on th book, why not try one of the other titles in the series?